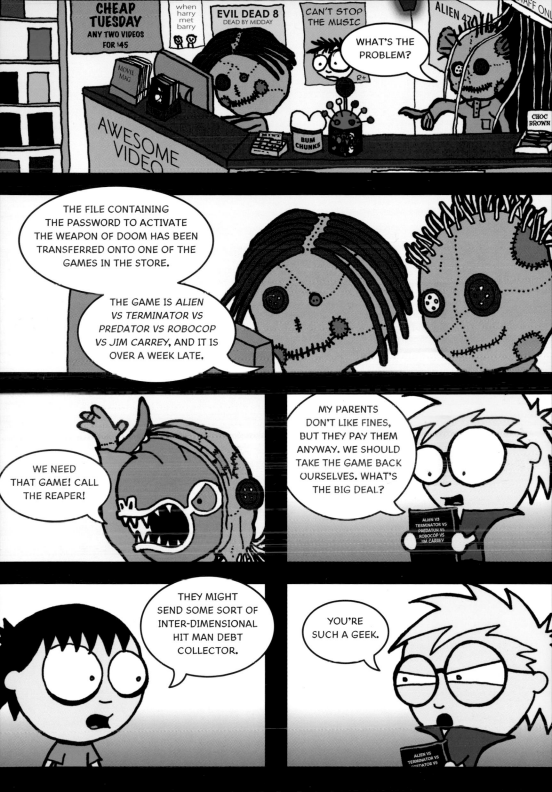

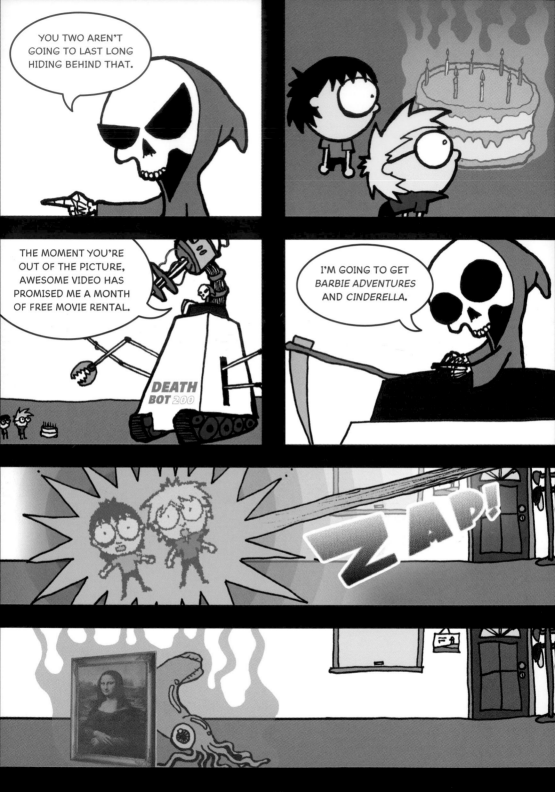

END OF CHAPTER TWO

34

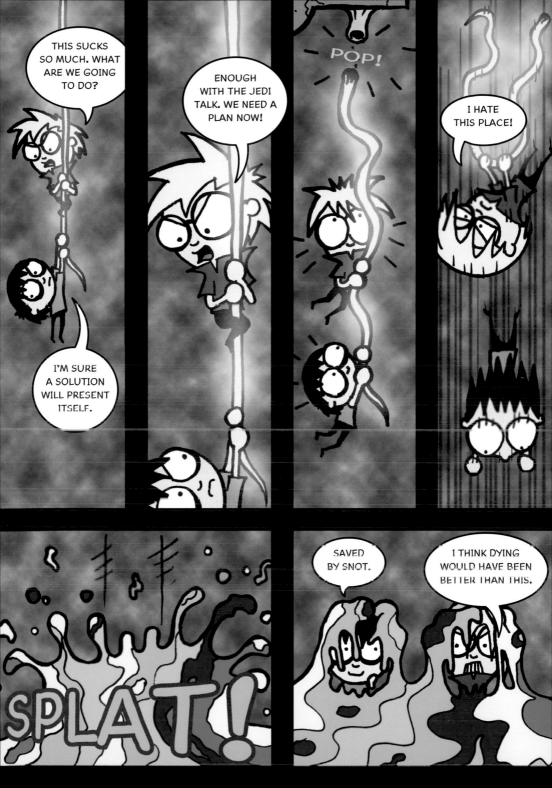

BOOOM!

WHERE ARE WE?

OOPS. WE SQUASHED THE CITY.

DID YOU SLAY THE MOUNTAIN GIANT?

WHO WANTS TO KNOW?

42

END OF CHAPTER THREE

45

DID YOU GUYS ENJOY YOUR MEAL?

IT WAS RAD.

A MEAL FIT FOR A KING.

NO! MY STUPID MEAL ATTACKED ME.

WHAT'S THIS THING, MR INTERNET?

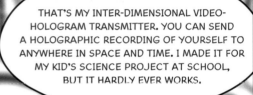

THAT'S MY INTER-DIMENSIONAL VIDEO-HOLOGRAM TRANSMITTER. YOU CAN SEND A HOLOGRAPHIC RECORDING OF YOURSELF TO ANYWHERE IN SPACE AND TIME. I MADE IT FOR MY KID'S SCIENCE PROJECT AT SCHOOL, BUT IT HARDLY EVER WORKS.

SEND A MESSAGE TO US IN THE PAST, AND TELL US TO TAKE THE GAME BACK.

IF WE'D RETURNED THE GAME, WE WOULDN'T BE STUCK IN THIS CRAZY WORLD!

SEEMS LIKE ALL I HAVE TO DO IS SET THE TIME AND PLACE, THEN PRESS RECORD.

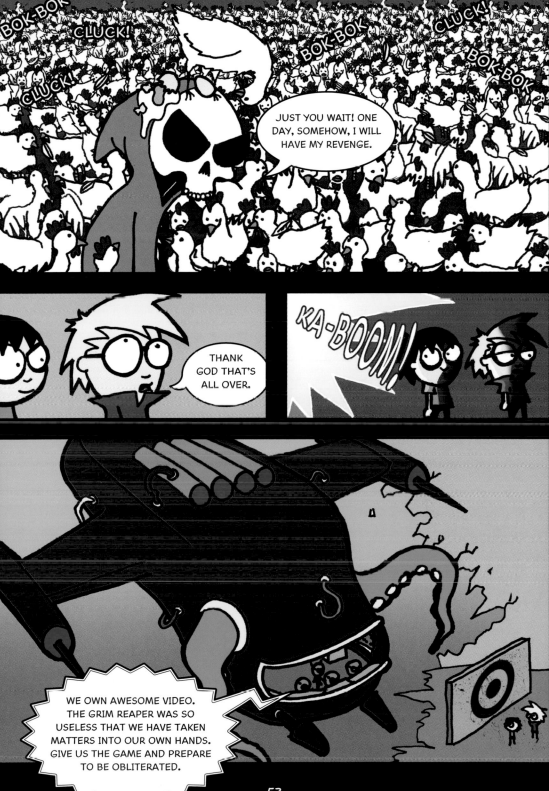

55

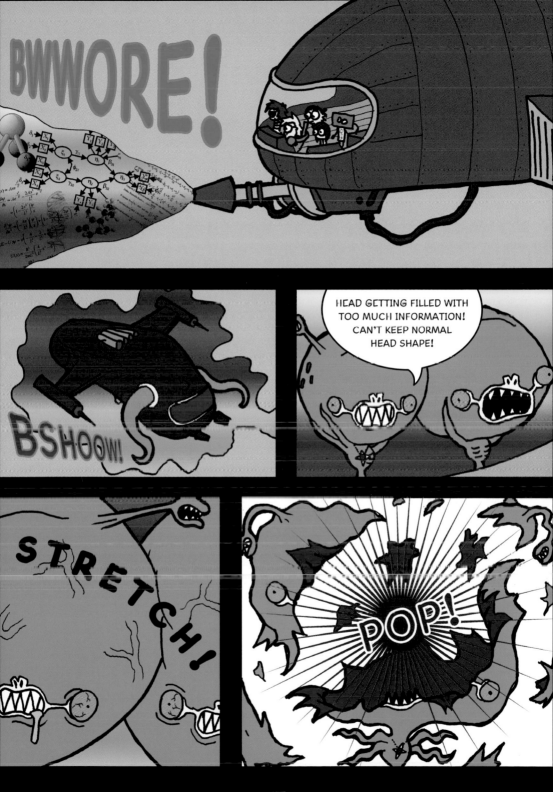

AFTERWORD

LOOK OUT FOR PILOT AND HUXLEY IN THEIR NEXT ADVENTURE!

DAN McGUINESS WAS DISCOVERED AS AN INFANT AMONG THE SMOULDERING REMAINS OF A TOP-SECRET LABORATORY.

HE GREW UP UNDER CLOSE SCRUTINY IN A MILITARY FACILITY OF UNCERTAIN LOCATION.

THE ARMY'S TOP SCIENTISTS ATTEMPTED TO HARNESS HIS EXTRAORDINARY POWERS OF STIR-FRY COOKERY AND REACHING THINGS ON HIGH SHELVES.

WHEN NOT HOOKED UP TO ELECTRODES, HE CAN BE FOUND IN HIS QUARTERS MANICALLY SCRIBBLING COMICS ONTO LOLLY WRAPPERS, SCRAPS OF TOILET PAPER, OR WHATEVER HE CAN GET HIS HANDS ON.

THOSE PAGES ARE COMPILED HERE AS HIS FIRST PUBLISHED BOOK, *PILOT & HUXLEY*.